LOAN EXHIBITION

# Cézanne

*Under the Patronage of*
*Mrs. Dwight D. Eisenhower and*
*His Excellency, Monsieur Hervé Alphand,*
*The Ambassador of France to the United States*

for the benefit of
The National Organization of
Mentally Ill Children

———

November 5 — December 5, 1959

## Wildenstein

19 East 64th Street, New York

THE NATIONAL ORGANIZATION FOR MENTALLY ILL CHILDREN, INC. acknowledges the devotion and invaluable services of the many friends who are responsible for the success of this exhibition. In behalf of severely disturbed and mentally ill children who benefit from its program, NOMIC is deeply grateful for the interest and support of Mrs. Dwight D. Eisenhower, Honorary Chairman and His Excellency, Monsieur Hervé Alphand, The Ambassador of France to the United States.

## HONORARY COMMITTEE

Dr. and Mrs. Harry Bakwin

Mr. and Mrs. Leonard Bernstein

Mr. Richard F. Brown
Chief Curator of Art
Los Angeles County Museum

Mr. John P. Coolidge
Director, Fogg Museum of Art

Dr. Harry Emerson Fosdick
Riverside Church

Dr. Alfred M. Frankfurter

Monsignor George H. Guilfoyle
Executive Director of
Catholic Charities

Mr. René d'Harnoncourt
Director
Museum of Modern Art, New York

Monsieur Raymond Laporte
Minister Plenipotentiary
Consul General of France
New York

Mr. Sherman E. Lee
Director
The Cleveland Museum of Art

The Hon. and Mrs. Herbert H. Lehman

The Hon. Henry Cabot Lodge
United States Ambassador to the U. N.

Mr. Henri Marceau
Director, Philadelphia Museum of Art

Rev. Dr. Julius Mark
Congregation Emanu-El

Rev. Robert J. McCracken
Riverside Church

Miss Agnes Mongan
Acting Director and Curator
Fogg Museum of Art

Monsieur Edouard Morot-Sir
Cultural Counselor to the
French Embassy

Mr. Charles P. Parkhurst
Director, Dudley Peter Allen
Memorial Art Museum
Oberlin College

Mr. Robert O. Parks
Director
Smith College Museum of Art

Mr. Perry T. Rathbone
Director, Museum of Fine Arts, Boston

Mr. John Rewald

Mrs. Franklin D. Roosevelt

Mr. James J. Rorimer
Director, Metropolitan Museum of Art

Mr. Laurence Sickman
Director
William Rockhill Nelson Gallery of Art
Kansas City

Mr. Gordon M. Smith
Director, Albright Art Gallery
Buffalo

Mr. James J. Sweeney, Director
The Solomon R. Guggenheim Museum

The Hon. and Mrs. Robert F. Wagner

Mr. Otto Wittmann
Director, Toledo Museum of Art

Mr. Carl Zigrosser
Acting Director
Philadelphia Museum of Art

Mr. Vladimir Visson
*Secretary to the Exhibit*

Mrs. Nicholas M. Schenck, Art Committee Chairman

Mrs. Victor S. Noerdlinger

and

Mrs. Benjamin Rosenbloom, Co-Chairmen,

as well as to the

Members of the Art Committee

SPECIAL THANKS ARE DUE TO THE LENDERS WHOSE
GENEROSITY HAS MADE THIS EXHIBITION POSSIBLE:

Albright Art Gallery, Buffalo

The Dudley Peter Allen Memorial Art Museum, Oberlin College

The Baltimore Museum of Art

The Art Institute of Chicago

The Cincinnati Art Museum

The Cleveland Museum of Art

Fogg Museum of Art, Harvard University, Cambridge, Mass.

Los Angeles County Museum

Marion Koogler McNay Art Institute, San Antonio

The Minneapolis Institute of Arts

The Montreal Museum of Fine Arts, Canada

Museum of Fine Arts, Boston

The Museum of Modern Art, New York

The William Rockhill Nelson Gallery of Art, Kansas City

Philadelphia Museum of Art

The Smith College Museum of Art, Northampton, Mass.

Toledo Museum of Art

We also wish to express our sincerest thanks to Dr. Meyer Schapiro for contributing the foreword to the catalogue and to Messrs. Daniel Wildenstein and Georges Wildenstein and their staff for their most generous cooperation in organizing this exhibition.

# FOREWORD

AFTER fifty years of the most radical change in art from images to free abstraction, Cézanne's painting, which looks old-fashioned today in its attachment to nature, maintains itself fresh and stimulating to young painters of our time. He has produced no school, but he has given an impulse directly or indirectly to almost every new movement since he died. His power to excite artists of different tendency and temperament is due, I think, to the fact that he realized with equal fullness so many different sides of his art. It has often been true of leading modern painters that they developed a single idea with great force. Some one element or expressive note has been worked out with striking effect. In Cézanne we are struck rather by the comprehensive character of his art, although later artists have built on a particular element of his style. Color, drawing, modelling, structure, touch and expression — if any of these can be isolated from the others — are carried to a new height in his work. He is arresting through his images — more rich in suggestive content than has been supposed — and also through his uninterpreted strokes which make us see that there can be qualities of greatness in little touches of paint. In his pictures single patches of the brush reveal themselves as an uncanny choice, deciding the unity of a whole region of forms. Out of these emerges a moving semblance of a familiar natural world with a deepened harmony that invites meditation. His painting is a balanced art, not in the sense that it is stabilized or moderate in its effects, but that opposed qualities are joined in a scrupulously controlled play. He is inventive and perfect in many different aspects of his art.

In this striving for fullness, Cézanne is an heir of the renaissance and baroque masters. Like Delacroix, he retains from Rubens and the Italians a concept of the grand — not in the size of the canvas but in the weight and complexity of variation. His grandeur is without rhetoric and convention, and inheres in the dramatic power of large contrasts and in the frankness of his means. His detached contemplation of his subjects arises from a passionate aspiring nature that seeks to master its own impulses through an objective attitude to things. The mountain peak is a natural choice for him, as is the abandoned quarry, the solitary house or tree, and the diversity of humble, impersonal objects on the table.

The greatness of Cézanne does not lie only in the perfection of single masterpieces; it is also in the quality of his whole achievement. An exhibition of works spanning his forty years as a painter reveals a remarkable inner freedom. The lives of Gauguin and van Gogh have blinded the public to what is noble and complete in Cézanne's less sensational, though anguished, career. Outliving these younger contemporaries, more fortunate in overcoming impulses and situations dangerous to art, he was able to mature more fully and to realize many more of his artistic ideas.

Cézanne's masterliness includes, besides the control of the canvas in its complexity and novelty, the ordering of his own life as an artist. His art has a unique quality of ripeness and continuous growth. While concentrating on his own problems — problems he had set himself and not taken from a school or leader — he was capable of an astonishing variety. This variety rests on the openness of his sensitive spirit. He admitted to the canvas a great span of perception and mood, greater than that of his impressionist friends. This is evident from the range of themes alone; but it is clear in the painterly qualities as well. He draws or colors; he composes or follows his immediate sensation of nature; he paints with a virile brush solidly, or in the most delicate sparse water color, and is equally sure in both. He possessed a firm faith in spontaneous sensibility, in the resources of the sincere self. He can be passionate and cool, grave and light; he is always honest.

Cézanne's work not only gives us the joy of beautiful painting; it appeals as an example of heroism in art. For he reached perfection, it is well known, in a long and painful struggle with himself. This struggle can be read in his work in the many signs of destructiveness and black moods, especially in his early phase; perhaps we may recognize it too even in the detached aspect of the world that he finally shapes into a serenely ordered whole. I do not doubt that the personal content of this classic art will in time become as evident as the aesthetic result.

MEYER SCHAPIRO

# Paul Cézanne

## 1839-1906

## HIS LIFE

1839      Paul Cézanne was born at 28 RUE DE L'OPÉRA, AIX-EN-PROVENCE on the 19th of January.

1839-1849      Already as a child he gave proof of a violent, irascible and uncontrollable temper. He attended a public school. At this time, according to his sister he did *Le Pont Mirabeau,* a drawing in charcoal, greatly admired by his family.

1850-1860      Cézanne became a pupil at the PENSIONNAT SAINT-JOSEPH directed by the ABBÉ SAVOURNIN. Highly sensitive and imaginative, the child was much impressed by the religious instruction he received. At the time of his first Communion, the symbolism of the ceremony, the mystery of the dogma stirred his soul, and gave him that vibrant faith which he kept to his death.

     Next followed the COLLÈGE BOURBON; here he became the inseparable companion of EMILE ZOLA and BAPTISTE BAILLE. Upon graduation, Cézanne announced to his father his desire to be a painter, and to join ZOLA in PARIS, but was persuaded to take up law instead. However, his father, condescended to give him a studio on the top floor of their country house, JAS DE BOUFFAN. Cézanne also frequented the local art school.

1861-1864      Again Cézanne was seized by the idea of going to PARIS; this time he was insistent and we find him in the capital chaperoned by his father and sister MARIE. Following the advice of ZOLA, he attended the ACADÉMIE SUISSE and spent a great deal of time in the LOUVRE. But lacking the stamina to face the discouragement of a hard, ruthless PARIS and longing for his beloved Southern PROVENCE he returned to AIX.

1865-1867      Cézanne entered his father's banking business but his heart was not in it. Yet LOUIS-AUGUSTE was rather tolerant of his son's artistic aspirations, knowing him to be of thrifty nature, with a prospect of a financially secure future. But despite an easy care-free life, the misanthropy of Cézanne increased with time; he became impossible to live with and he returned to PARIS. Back at the ACADÉMIE SUISSE he met PISSARRO who had a great influence on Cézanne and encouraged him in his work. It is in this period that the young painter failed the entrance examination for the ECOLE DES-BEAUX-ARTS. This fact embittered him greatly and he never ceased to despise and insult this institution—"CES BOZARTS"—in his broad provençal brogue. GUILLEMET introduced Cézanne to BAZILLE, who in turn took him to meet FANTIN and RENOIR in their studios. Cézanne painted quite often at the side of the painters who later on were to be known as IMPRESSIONISTS. In 1863 he exhibited at the SALON DES REFUSÉS with his newly discovered friends. In 1866 he tried in vain to establish another SALON DES REFUSÉS, but met with government opposition. Though more adjusted to Parisian life, Cézanne still preferred the solitary hours spent in the LOUVRE copying a a RIBERA or RUBENS to the animated literary and aesthetic discussions in the smoky atmosphere of the CAFE GUERBOIS. His exaggerated opinions, his social awkwardness and his fits of temper branded him as an eccentric even among the bohemian rebels of art. Embittered and nervous he returned to AIX where he worked hard and steadily.

1868-1869    Restless, the painter moved from one place to another; first in PARIS, from RUE DE CHEVREUSE to the RUE DE VAUGIRARD; then in PROVENCE, from L'ESTAQUE to AIX. More and more he tended toward seclusion.

1870-1871    The Franco-Prussian War forced Cézanne to leave PARIS, to go to L'ESTAQUE, PERTUIS and AIX. He evaded the draft, but at this time military service was not compulsory. At the end of the war, Cézanne returned to PARIS to find his friends were back again, all save BAZILLE who had been killed in the battle.

1872    Again Cézanne changed his address in PARIS and lived near the JARDIN DES PLANTES. Next, on the advice of PISSARRO he settled in AUVERS-SUR-OISE, where he met DR. GACHET who immediately was won over by Cézanne's paintings. Later GACHET became a friend of another painter of genius, VAN GOGH, a man hated and scorned by Cézanne.

1873-1877    Again Cézanne nervously changed his place of habitat, living successively in PARIS, and during the summers in AUVERS, ST. OUEN-L'AUMONE or PONTOISE. The majority of the painters now called IMPRESSIONISTS had been able from time to time to exhibit at the SALON despite the numerous setbacks, but not Cézanne. Moreover, no dealer would handle his pictures. Thus, he joyfully welcomed the chance to exhibit independently of the SALON, and he participated in the first Exhibition of the IMPRESSIONISTS in 1874. The fiasco of this exhibition is well known; the greatest share of abuse went to Cézanne. Yet two well-known collectors, DORIA and CHOCQUET, purchased Cézanne's paintings. To add to his misfortunes even DEGAS could not restrain his natural sarcasm in the criticism of the art of his colleague. Cézanne exhibited with the Impressionists again in 1877. After that, for almost twenty years the public very seldom saw the master's work.

1878-1879    Cézanne spent this year at L'ESTAQUE and AIX.

1879-1880    Driven on by his restlessness, he lived at MELUN and on the banks of the SEINE.

1881-1887    During this period the painter was rarely seen in PARIS. He stayed at LA ROCHE-GUYON with RENOIR, in MÉDAN with EMILE ZOLA, at HATTENVILLE in NORMANDY with CHOCQUET, but most of his time he spent in PROVENCE, at AIX, L'ESTAQUE and GARDANNE. In 1882 his friend, GUILLEMET, succeeded in having the SALON accept a small portrait by Cézanne; however this canvas passed unnoticed.

1888-1889    Cézanne again moved to PARIS and took quarters in an old hotel in QUAI D'ANJOU; CHOCQUET, his patron, arranged to have his work admitted to the SALON of 1889, but again with no result. Hurt, and aloof and savage Cézanne withdraws into an ivory tower.

After living two years in PARIS with summer trips to the banks of the MARNE, to CHANTILLY and PROVENCE, the painter again changed his place of residence in the capital to AVENUE D'ORLÉANS.

1890-1894    Cézanne lived successively in AIX, FONTAINEBLEAU and in FRANCHE-COMTÉ. He visited SWITZERLAND; but this country left no impression on his work. During this period Cézanne exhibited some canvases in BRUSSELS with the progressive group of Les XX; there he was discovered by several critics—GEORGES LECOMTE, GUSTAVE GEOFFROY and the painter MAURICE DENIS, all of whom praised his work even though with considerable reserve. Cézanne's paintings were beginning to sell, but they brought only a few hundred francs, as at the sale of the estate of the late PÈRE TANGUY. It is also at this time that the state refused to accept the Cézannes included in the CAILLEBOTTE collection which had been presented by the owner to the MUSÉE DU LUXEMBOURG.

| 1895 | Cézanne returned to PARIS, because that most perceptive of art dealers, VOLLARD, decided to give the painter a one-man show in his galleries on RUE LAFFITTE. The critics were surprised, if not enthusiastic; but for the first time they were not overly hostile. Cézanne was for most of them merely a newcomer. His secluded life and his financial security had prevented him from creating as much noise as some of the other revolutionary painters who were forced to call attention to themselves in order to gain recognition and sell their works. |
|---|---|
| 1896-1899 | Again Cézanne changed domicile and moved to the RUE DES DAMES and seemed at this time to lose some of his misanthropy. He traveled to GIVERNY, to VICHY, to ANNECY, and spent his summers at MONTGEROULT, MARINES and MARLOTTES. In the winter time he stayed in PARIS and, of course, in AIX. |
|  | In 1897 Cézanne lost his beloved mother. At her death JAS DE BOUFFAN was sold; this also hurt him deeply. To console himself he built a new studio surrounded by gardens—LES LAUVES—in the vicinity of AIX. |
| 1899-1906 | During these last years, Cézanne, except for a short three-month period, lived in his native city. If he did not travel more extensively, it was not because he had lost his wanderlust, but because of the sickness which had been undermining him for a long time, making travel extremely painful. He led a simple, retired life, filled with intense work. |
|  | Despite his wanderings and absence from PARIS, during the period of 1899-1902 his fame was growing. He now exhibited regularly at the SALON DES INDÉPENDANTS. In 1900 he participated in the EXPOSITION UNIVERSELLE de PARIS. In these last few years Cézanne had made progress with public opinion. Foreign museums were showing his paintings; he had the admiration of young painters such as MAURICE DENIS, ODILON REDON, BONNARD, and VUILLARD. His atelier, LES LAUVES, had become a sort of shrine of modern art. |
|  | Age and sickness, however, could not diminish Cézanne's enthusiasm and persistence in his work. In mid-October, while painting outdoors, he was caught in a violent storm. He fainted on his way home and was picked up by a passing driver. Cézanne developed pneumonia and died on the 22nd of October, 1906, in AIX-EN-PROVENCE, alone, as he had lived. |

# THE MAN

A few quotations of Cézanne himself should be revelatory of the nature of the man and his philosophy. The instability of Cézanne's character, its mixture of shyness and impatience, ferocity and insecurity, and his neurotic fear of people made him a misanthrope and brought about his gradual withdrawal from society.

> *"I am a timid man, a bohemian, and people laugh at me. I have no power of resistance; isolation, that is what I am worthy of. At least that way no one will put his hooks into me."*

> *"To work and not worry about anybody and to become strong, that is the aim of the artist; the rest is not worth the* Mot de Cambronne . . ." *"Compared to me, my compatriots are asses, I detest them all."*

Cézanne was deeply religious, and his friend Emile Bernard wrote:

> *"A true believer, Cézanne thought that he would find in the here-after his reward; he felt this was coming to him for he had made a sacrifice of his life with the sublime abandon of a voluntary martyr."*

He never attempted to use his brush in the service of his faith. When asked to paint Christ he answered:

> *"I would be afraid; first, that has been done by our great masters, and besides, it would be too difficult."*

Cézanne's sobriety was exceptional, a trait which distinguished him from the rest of his friends:

> *"Daumier drank too much. What a great master he would have been without that!"*

Of great modesty, he once, towards the end of his life, told Emile Bernard, on seeing one of his own early works:

> *"It is quite bad; is that what they admire in Paris today? Well, the rest must be pretty poor."*

Extremely chaste, he would not have female models. In later years he used the drawings he had made at the Académie Suisse forty years before!

> *"I have always used these drawings, they are not quite satisfactory, but at my age . . ."*

Cézanne had no ear for music, and capriciously liked Wagner for the sound of his name. He had a greater understanding of literature; he liked Baudelaire, and his own rather numerous poems show the influence of that poet. He had great respect for authority, for official art, official places of exhibition and for public recognition:

> *"Mostly I admire Couture, Delacroix and Granet, but above all, Couture who is a great and veritable master."*
> *"I would love to be admitted to the Salon of Bouguereau. I know well that the fault lies not with my vision, but in my inability to realize it."*

He insisted on the importance of tradition:

> *"The Louvre is a book which teaches us how to read."*
> *"I am troubled by the lack of materialization of my ideas. I shall perhaps fulfill that wish, but I am old, and it is possible that I will die without having reached that supreme goal: to realize as the Venetians."*

His judgment of other contemporary painters was hard:

> *"Gauguin is not a painter; but Pissarro approaches Nature. Renoir has created the woman of Paris, Monet has given a vision . . . what follows does not count."*

The artist was eternally hesitating between doubts as to his own ability, dissatisfaction, feelings of frustration and a clear, definite idea of his own part as a painter:

> *"The artist addresses himself to a restricted number of individuals; he must beware of literary spirit and opinion which so often cause painting to deviate from its true path—the concrete study of nature."*

He wrote to Vollard:

> *"I have made some progress, why so late and so painfully?"*

and then again:

> *"I am becoming, as a painter, more lucid outdoors, but indoors the realization of my sensations is increasingly difficult. I cannot achieve the intensity which my senses develop. I do not possess that richness of coloring which animates Nature."*

In spite of his admiration for the art of the past, he used it only as a stepping stone. He wanted to *"leave the memory of the museums behind and strive for personal expression."*

Cézanne considered himself as a primitive of a new art he felt to be in progress. He borrowed only the absolute minimum, he was not an imitator:

> *"I want to do Poussin entirely over from nature, that is the classic which I understand."*

> *"I did not imitate Pissarro and Monet any more than I imitated the great ones of the Louvre. I tried to do my own work—a sincere work, naïve, according to my ability and my vision."*

# HIS PAINTING

Let us examine the complexity of Cézanne's palette. In 1900, according to Emile Bernard it was as follows:

Yellows:     Brilliant Yellow—Yellow of Naples—Chrome Yellow— Yellow Ochre—Raw Siena

Reds:     Vermillion—Red Ochre—Burnt Siena—Deep Madder— Crimson Lake—Burnt Carmine

Greens:     Veronese Green—Emerald Green—Terra Verte

Blues:     Cobalt Blue—Ultramarine—Prussian Blue—Blue Black

The composition of his palette strangely enough approaches that of Rubens or Delacroix and by the breadth of its range differs violently from the palette of the Impressionists. A fervent disciple of Delacroix, Cézanne systematized the former's principle that *"all fields of color are enriched by their own shading."*

According to Cézanne, *"In an orange, an apple, a bowl, there is a culminating point; and this point is always—in spite of tremendous effects of light and shade and colorful sensations—the closest to our eyes; the edges of the objects recede to a center on our horizon. . . ."* It is by the tonal gradations of his variegated palette, used in gentle succession, that Cézanne makes the edges recede and arrives at the volume of his objects. He models by modulation. The tonal gradations he establishes according to the prismatic law and thus no voids develop on his canvas. But it is not enough to modulate a color; he finds that a certain quantity of bluish tints is necessary to give life to other colors and he distributes them on his canvas.

Unlike the Impressionists, Cézanne did not try to paint light alone; light for him was only a function of local color. He says himself, *"I know nothing except color. Light is but the tone of a place, shadow is another. . . ."* For this reason, he excludes all agents that might produce light, shadow or reflection. He says further, *"An optical impression is produced on our organs by light which makes us classify as light, half-tone or quarter-tone, the surfaces represented by color sensa-tions."* Thus, each surface of light in nature is translated by the artist into a plane of color. He does not use aerial or linear perspective, he achieves depth by a carefully calculated shifting of these color planes.

He also gradually perfects a technique which allows him to achieve an even greater feeling of the three-dimensional. He breaks his color surfaces down into small areas slanted at different angles and painted with small, elongated brush strokes running parallel to one another. This is what is known as Cézanne's *petite sensation.*

*"The painter,"* Cézanne says, *"must rely on his vision. He must do everything according to nature with much reflection, because every color-touch must contain air, light, the object, the plan, the character, the drawing and the style; in a word, all that which constitutes a painting."* Air and light, as discussed above, are to Cézanne, of secondary importance. It is also the essence of the object, its character, its eternal stability and solidity rather than its momentary aspects which are of primary concern to the painter. Hence, his indifference to subject-matter and its lack of variety—his innumerable apples and mountains.

Volume and depth, Cézanne insists, exists not only through drawing and per-spective, but should emerge from the color itself; these he achieves primarily through the composition of his color planes and his tonal gradations.

The painter does not hesitate to simplify and distort against his own predilections in order completely to realize his artistic aim—his style.

Cézanne, who throughout his career was groping for tradition, revived the science of tonality of Delacroix and the search of form of Poussin, and thus transcended the limitations and the shimmering, atmospheric surfaces of Impressionism.

# CATALOGUE

1. *Portrait de Louis-Auguste Cézanne,* 1860-63          66⅜ x 44⅞ inches
        *Father of the Artist*          V. 25
              Lent by Mr. Raymond Pitcairn


"V." refers to the Venturi numbers in his Catalogue Raisonné *Cezanne,* Paris, 1936.

2. *Nature Morte: Le Pain et Les Oeufs,* 1865          23¼ x 30 inches

V. 59

Lent by The Cincinnati Art Museum

3. *L'Oncle Dominique,* 1865-67       16¼ x 13 inches
V. 76

Lent by Dr. and Mrs. Harry Bakwin

4. *L'Oncle Dominique,* 1865-67

18¼ x 15 inches
V. 79

Lent by Mrs. A. L. Spitzer

5.  *Route Tournante en Provence,* 1867-70          36 x 28 inches
                                                    V. 53

Lent by The Montreal Museum of Fine Arts

6. *Portrait Romantique,* 1868-70        19½ x 17½ inches

V. 97

Lent by Dr. and Mrs. Harry Bakwin

7. *Louveciennes,* 1872

28¾ x 36¼ inches
V. 153

Lent Anonymously

8.  *Paysage à Pontoise.*  1873-77                    17½ x 21 inches
                                                      V. 154

Lent by Mr. Stanley S. Snellenburg

9. *Les Petites Maisons à Auvers*, 1873-74        15¾ x 21½ inches
V. 156

Lent by The Fogg Museum of Art

10. *Scène Fantastique,* 1873-75          21½ x 32 inches
                                          V. 243

Lent by Mr. and Mrs. Howard B. White

11.  *L'Eternel Féminin,* 1875-77                    17 x 21 inches
                                                      V. 247

Lent by Mr. Harold Hecht

12.  *La Lutte d'Amour,* 1875-76              15 x 18¼ inches
                                                        V. 384
                  Lent by The Hon. and Mrs. W. Averell Harriman

13. *Les Baigneurs au Repos,* 1875-76                      15 x 18 inches

V. 273

Lent by Mrs. Nate B. Spingold

14.  *Compotier et Assiette de Biscuits,* c. 1877          20⅞ x 24¾ inches

V. 209

Lent by Mr.and Mrs. Edwin C. Vogel

15. *Sancho dans l'Eau*, c. 1877

18½ x 21⅝ inches
V. 239

Lent by Wildenstein & Co.

16. *Un Village,* 1879-82                    23⅝ x 28¾ inches
                                             V. 307

Lent by Mr. and Mrs. William Goetz

17. *La Campagne d'Auvers*, 1879-82

Lent by Mr. Basil Goulandris

36¼ x 28¾ inches
V. 312

18.  *Maison au Bord du Chemin*, 1879-82       21¼ x 17¾ inches

V. 328

Lent by Mr. and Mrs. David Rosenthal

19. *La Route Tournante,* 1879-82

$23\frac{1}{2}$ x $28\frac{1}{2}$ inches
V. 329

Lent by The Museum of Fine Arts, Boston

20.  *La Maison Rustique*, 1879-82             23½ x 28¾ inches
V. 331

Collection of Mark Eisner

21. *Femme à la Fourrure*, 1879-82

21 x 19¼ inches
V. 376

Lent Anonymously

22. *Le Viaduc à l'Estaque,* 1882-85        17¼ x 21 inches

V. 401

Lent by the Allen Memorial Art Museum, Oberlin College

23.  *Paysage d'Aix en Provence*, 1885

25½ x 21½ inches
V. 416

Lent by Mr. and Mrs. Aaron W. Davis

24. *Le Bassin du Jas de Bouffan,* 1882-85

29 x 32½ inches
V. 417

Lent by The Albright Art Gallery

25. *Sous-Bois,* 1882-85                45¾ x 31⅞ inches
V. 419

Lent by Dr. and Mrs. Harry Bakwin

26. *Route Tournante à la Roche-Guyon,* 1885          29¾ x 24½ inches

V. 441

Lent by The Smith College Museum of Art

27. *Nature Morte: Cerises et Pêches,* 1883-87          19½ x 24 inches
                                                         V. 498

Lent by Dr. and Mrs. David M. Levy

28.  *Portrait de l'Artiste,* 1883-85                    10 x 10 inches
                                                         V. 517

Lent by Mr. Basil Goulandris

29. *Baigneuses,* 1883-87

13¾ x 15½ inches
V. 547

Lent by Mrs. H. Harris Jonas

30. *Portrait de Madame Cézanne,* 1883-87

18 x 15 inches
V. 526

Lent by Mr. Louis E. Stern

31. *Le Jas de Bouffan*, 1885-87

29¼ x 21½ inches
V. 470

Lent Anonymously

32. *Maison aux Toits Rouges, Jas de Bouffan*, 1885-87     28¾ x 36¼ inches

V. 468

Lent by Mrs. Georg S. Hirschland

33. *Marronniers du Jas de Bouffan*, 1885-87　　　　28¾ x 36¼ inches

V. 476

Lent by The Minneapolis Institute of Arts

34.  *Nature Morte: Pommes,*  1885-87                     15 x 18 inches

V. 501

Lent by Mr. and Mrs. Alex M. Lewyt

35. *Portrait de Madame Cézanne au Fauteuil Jaune*, 1890-94    32 x 25½ inches
                                                                 V. 571

Lent by Mr. and Mrs. John L. Loeb

36. *La Préparation du Banquet,* c. 1890      17¾ x 21 inches
                       V. 586

Lent by Mrs. Irene Mayer Selznick

37.  *Nature Morte: Bouilloire et Fruits*, 1890-94          19¾ x 24 inches
                                                            V. 615

Lent by Dr. and Mrs. Harry Bakwin

38. *Vase de Tulipes,* 1890-94        23 x 16½ inches

V. 617

Lent by The Art Institute of Chicago

39.  *Les Grosses Pommes,* 1890-94                    18⅜ x 22 inches
                                                       V. 621

Lent  Anonymously

40.  *La Maison Abandonnée,* 1892-94                    19¾ x 24 inches
                                                        V. 659

Lent by Mr. Ralph M. Coe

41. *Clairière, 1892-96*                    39½ x 32 inches
                                            V. 670

Lent by The Toledo Museum of Art

42. *La Montagne Sainte-Victoire,* 1894-1900          25¾ x 35½ inches
V. 666

Lent by The Cleveland Museum of Art,
(Bequest of Leonard C. Hanna, Jr.)

43. *Homme aux Bras Croisés*, 1895-1900    36¼ x 28¾ inches
V. 685

Lent by Cdr. and Mrs. Carleton Mitchell

44. *L'Enfant au Chapeau de Paille*, 1896                     27¼ x 22¾ inches
                                                              V. 700

Lent by The Los Angeles County Museum

45.  *Jeune Italienne Accoudée*, c. 1896          36¼ x 28¾ inches
                                                  V. 701

x

Lent by Dr. and Mrs. Harry Bakwin

46. *Portrait d'Henri Gasquet,* 1896-97          21¾ x 18⅛ inches
                                                          V. 695
Lent by The Marion Koogler McNay Art Institute, San Antonio

47.  *Nu Féminin,* c. 1895

36½ x 28 inches
V. 710

Lent  Anonymously

48.  *Nature Morte aux Oranges,* 1895-1900          23¾ x 28¾ inches
                                                     V. 738
         Lent by The Museum of Modern Art, New York
                  (Lillie P. Bliss Collection)

49. *La Montagne Sainte-Victoire, Vue de Bibemus*, 1898-1900    25⅝ x 31⅞ inches
V. 766

Lent by The Baltimore Museum of Art
(Etta Cone Collection)

50.  *Carrière de Bibemus*, 1898-1900             25⅝ x 31⅞ inches
                                                    V. 767
                  Lent by Mr. and Mrs. Siegfried Kramarsky

51. *Rochers dans le Parc du Château Noir,* c. 1900         24 x 32 inches

V. 784

Lent by Mrs. H. Harris Jonas

52.  *Route Tournante en Sous-Bois,* 1900-06                32 x 25½ inches
                                                            V. 789

Lent by Dr. and Mrs. Harry Bakwin

53. *Sous-Bois Provençal*, 1900-06                                    32 x 24⅞ inches
                                                                       V. 791

                              Lent by The Albright Art Gallery

54. *La Montagne Sainte-Victoire,* 1904-06        27⅞ x 36⅛ inches
V. 798

Lent by The Philadelphia Museum of Art
(George W. Elkins Collection)

55.  *La Montagne Sainte-Victoire,* 1904-1906          25½ x 32 inches
                                                       V. 800
          Lent by The William Rockhill Nelson Gallery of Art

56. *Maisons sur la Colline,* 1900-06                                   25¾ x 32 inches
                                                                          V. 1528
Lent by The Marion Koogler McNay Art Institute, San Antonio

# PASTELS, WATERCOLORS AND DRAWINGS

58.

57. *Femme Nue nouant ses Cheveux,* drawing, 1865-70    6½ x 9 inches
V. 1171

Lent by Mr. and Mrs. Philip Weisberg

58. *Fleurs,* pastel, 1873-74    7½ x 5¾ inches
V. Page 347

Lent by Mr. and Mrs. Dunbar W. Bostwick

60.

59. *Camille Pissarro,* drawing, c. 1873          3⅞ x 3⅛ inches
                    Lent by Mr. and Mrs. John Rewald

60. *Olympia,* watercolor, 1875-77          10 x 10¾ inches
                                                                    V. 882
                    Lent by Mr. Louis E. Stern

61. *La Côte du Galet,* watercolor, 1879-82    12 x 19 inches
Lent by Mr. and Mrs. Alex M. Lewyt


62. *Copie de L'Apothéose de Henry IV de Rubens,* drawing, 1880-90
$6\frac{1}{2}$ x $4\frac{1}{2}$ inches
Lent by Mr. and Mrs. John Rewald

63.  *Nature Morte: Pommes et Poires,* watercolor, 1883-87    9¾ x 12¾ inches
V. 1619

Lent by Mr. and Mrs. Alex M. Lewyt

64. *Portrait de l'Artiste,* drawing, c. 1885          10 x 10 inches

Lent by Mr. Walter C. Baker

65. *Portrait de Madame Cézanne,* drawing, 1885  6¾ x 4¾ inches

Lent by Mr. and Mrs. John Rewald

66. *Le Fils de Cézanne,* drawing, c. 1885          19¼ x 12¼ inches
V. 1469

Lent by Hillman Periodicals, Inc.

68.

67. *Environs de Gardanne,* watercolor, 1885-86      12¼ x 18½ inches

V. 907

Lent by Mr. and Mrs. F. H. Hirschland

68. *Le Verger,* watercolor, 1885-86      12⅝ x 18⅛ inches

V. 927

Lent by Mr. and Mrs. David M. Heyman

69. *Arbre Depouillé au Jas de Bouffan,* watercolor, 1885-87 13½ x 11½ inches
V. 941
Lent by Mr. and Mrs. Alex M. Lewyt

70. *Arbres,* watercolor, 1885-87 18¼ x 13¼ inches
V. 980
Lent by Mr. and Mrs. George Henry Warren

71. *La Maison,* watercolor, 1888-92 16¾ x 22½ inches
V. 960
Lent by Mr. and Mrs. F. H. Hirschland

72. *Le Parc,* watercolor, 1888-94 19 x 12 inches
V. 998
Lent by Mr. and Mrs. John W. Warrington

73. *Feuilles dans un Vase vert,* watercolor, 1885-95      17½ x 11¾ inches
V. 1117

Lent by Mr. and Mrs. Paul M. Hirschland

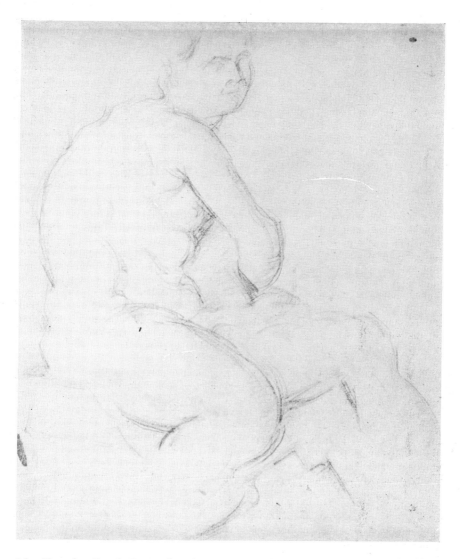

74. *Hercules d'après Puget,* drawing, 1888-95   8¼ x 7⅛ inches

Lent by Mr. and Mrs. John Rewald

75. *Maison sur la Colline, Environs d'Aix,* watercolor, 1890-94     18 x 22 inches
V. 976

Lent by Mr. Louis E. Stern

76. *Les Arbres,* watercolor, 1895-1900                          18 x 11¾ inches

Lent by Mr. and Mrs. Lazarus Phillips

77.  *Pins à Bibemus,* watercolor, 1895-1900        17½ x 11½ inches
                                                     V. 985
                Lent by Mr. and Mrs. John W. Warrington

78. *Rochers à Bibemus,* watercolor, 1895-1900     18½ x 14 inches
V. 1046

Lent by Col. Samuel A. Berger

79. *Hortensias,* watercolor, 1895-1900          19½ x 12¾ inches
                                                  V. 1069
              Lent by Mr. and Mrs. Siegfried Kramarsky

80.  *Pommes et Encrier,* watercolor, 1895-1900          12⅛ x 17¾ inches

Lent by Mr. and Mrs. Paul M. Hirschland

81. *Eglise dans un Village,* watercolor, 1900-04          17½ x 12¾ inches

Lent by Mr. Basil Goulandris

82. *La Montagne Sainte-Victoire,* watercolor, 1900-06

12⅝ x 19¾ inches
V. 1018

Lent by Dr. Sonja Kramarsky

83.  *Route Tournante,* watercolor, 1895-1904                12¼ x 18¾ inches
V. 1071
Lent by Mr. and Mrs. James Wood Johnson

84. *Vallée de l'Arc,* watercolor, 1904-06          9½ x 12¼ inches

Lent Anonymously

85. *La Rivière au Pont des Trois Sautets,* watercolor, 1906      16 x 21 inches
V. 1076

Lent by the Cincinnati Art Museum

86. *La Cathédrale d'Aix vue du Jardin des Lauves,* watercolor, 1904-06    12¼ x 18½ inches

V. 1077

Lent by Hillman Periodicals, Inc.

87.  *Portrait de Vallier,* watercolor, 1900-06          18¾ x 12¼ inches
V. 1092
Lent by Mr. and Mrs. Siegfried Kramarsky